Universal Edition

30 Easy Piano Studies

In classical, jazz and popular styles

Mike Cornick

Elementary to Intermediate level

www.universaledition.com

vienna · london · new york

UE 21 298

ISMN M-008-07674-9
UPC 8-03452-06036-9
ISBN 978-3-7024-2910-2

Preface

Few of today's piano teachers would choose to restrict their pupils' repertoire to the strictly 'classical' and this broadening of approach, to include the playing of pieces in a range of styles, is very clearly reflected in the syllabus selections of most examination boards.

With this in mind, the compilation of this new set of piano studies includes pieces with a Blues, Jazz or Latin feel, as well as the expected classically-styled exercises.

In this *elementary to intermediate* volume, the choice of key signatures has been restricted accordingly, i.e. major keys extending to 2 sharps or 2 flats together with their relative minor keys. The first section of the book consists of pieces which explore the scales of each of these keys.

The term 'study' can summon a very mixed range of emotions and I am hopeful that within this selection our pupils will find these pieces both attractive and stimulating as well as educative. Each piece primarily focuses on a particular technical and/or interpretative aspect of piano playing but there are, inevitably, overlapping areas of skill and knowledge from one section of the book to another.

Mike Cornick, September 2004

Performance Directions

The direction (♪♩ = ♪♩) means that quavers (eighth notes) are to be played evenly, as written.

The direction (♪♩ = ♩ ♪) means that quavers (eighth notes) are to be played with a swing feel.

E.g. ♩♪♩♪ should be played ♩ ♪♩ ♪

and ♪ ♪♩ should be played ♪ ♩ ♪

The degree of swing which the player applies to quaver (eighth note) movement, however, is a matter of interpretation and need not be treated with absolute mathematical precision.

Vorwort

Nur wenige Klavierlehrer würden heutzutage das Repertoire ihrer Schüler auf das streng „Klassische" beschränken wollen, und diese offenere Herangehensweise, die das Spielen von Stücken in verschiedenen Stilen fördert, spiegelt sich in der Wahl der Lehrplanstücke der meisten Prüfungskommissionen sehr deutlich wider.

Die hier vorliegende Sammlung von Klavierstudien berücksichtigt dies und enthält sowohl Stücke mit einem Blues-, Jazz oder Latin-Feeling als auch solche im traditionellen klassischen Stil.

Die Stücke sind in leichtem bis mittleren Schwierigkeitsgrad gehalten und die Tonarten wurden entsprechend angepasst, d. h. die Durtonarten und ihre jeweiligen Mollparallelen haben bis zu zwei Kreuz- oder B-Vorzeichen. Der erste Teil des Heftes besteht aus Stücken, in denen diese Tonarten geübt werden.

Der Begriff „Etüde" kann eine ganze Reihe verschiedener Gefühle wecken und ich hoffe, dass Schüler diese Stücke interessant, anregend und lehrreich finden. Jedes Stück konzentriert sich auf einen technischen und/oder gestalterischen Aspekt des Klavierspiels, es gibt aber zwangsläufig Überschneidungen zwischen den verschiedenen Abschnitten des Buches.

Mike Cornick, September 2004

Aufführungshinweise

Das Zeichen (♫ = ♫) bedeutet, dass die Achtelnoten genau so gespielt werden, wie sie notiert sind.

Das Zeichen (♫ = ♩♪) bedeutet, dass die Achtelnoten mit „Swing Feeling" gespielt werden.

D. h. ♫♫ sollte so gespielt werden ♩♪♩♪

und ♪♫ sollte so gespielt werden ♪♩♪

Das Maß an triolischer Rhythmisierung, das der Spieler der Achtelbewegung gibt, ist eine Frage der Interpretation und braucht nicht mit absoluter mathematischer Präzision behandelt zu werden.

Préface

Aujourd'hui, peu de professeurs de piano prendraient le parti de restreindre le répertoire de leurs élèves au seul domaine « classique ». Cet élargissement de l'approche qui inclut la pratique de pièces embrassant une grande variété de styles est très clairement reflété dans les sélections au programme de la plupart des conseils d'examen.

Partant de cette idée, la compilation de cette nouvelle série d'études pour piano ou clavier inclut des pièces manifestant un « toucher » blues, jazz ou latin marqué, de même que les exercices attendus de style classique.

Comme l'implique les termes « élémentaire à intermédiaire », le choix des tonalités a été fait en conséquence : les tonalités majeures s'étendant à 2 dièses ou 2 bémols avec leurs tonalités mineures correspondantes. La première partie de la partition consiste de pièces dans lesquelles ces tonalités sont étudiées.

Le terme « étude » peut résumer une grande variété de sentiments, et j'espère vivement que nos élèves trouveront ces pièces à la fois attrayantes, stimulantes et instructives. Chaque pièce se concentre sur un aspect technique particulier ou relatif à l'interprétation pianistique, mais inévitablement, d'une section du recueil à une autre se chevauchent des zones relatives à la dextérité et à la connaissance.

Mike Cornick, Septembre 2004

Indications pour l'exécution

Le signe (♪♩ = ♪♩) signifie que les croches doivent être jouées exactement comme elles sont notées.

Le signe (♪♩ = ♩♪) signifie que le croches sont jouées avec une « sensibilité swing ».

C'est-à-dire que ♩♩♩♩ devrait être joué ainsi ♩♪♩♪

et que ♪ ♩♩ devrait être joué ainsi ♪♩♪

Le degré de balancement que l'exécutant applique au mouvement de croche est, quoi qu'il en soit, une question d'interprétation et ne doit pas être traité avec une absolue précision mathématique.

Crossing the Bridge

Mike Cornick
(* 1947)

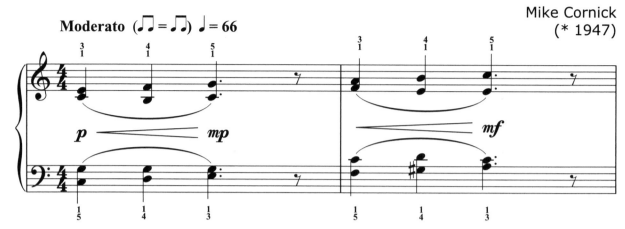

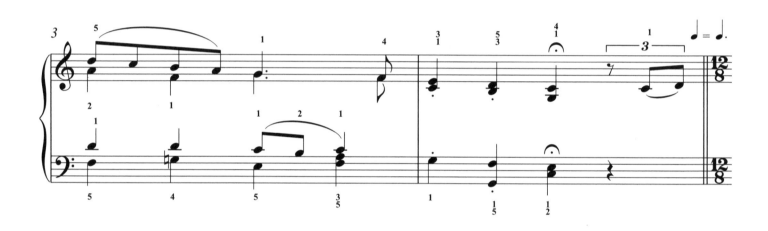

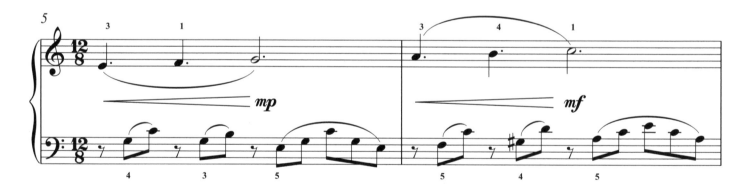

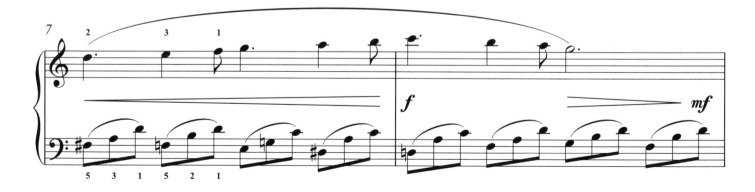

Universal Edition UE 21 298

Contrariwise

Mike Cornick
(* 1947)

Gliding

Mike Cornick
(* 1947)

Andante cantabile (♫ = ♫) ♩ = 104

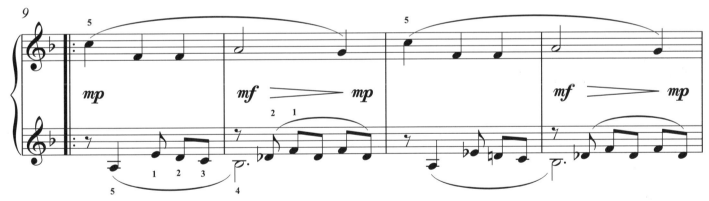

rall. (on repeat)

A Lyric Piece

Mike Cornick

Slowly and reflectively ($\sqcap$ = $\sqcap$) $\quad \downarrow$ = 84

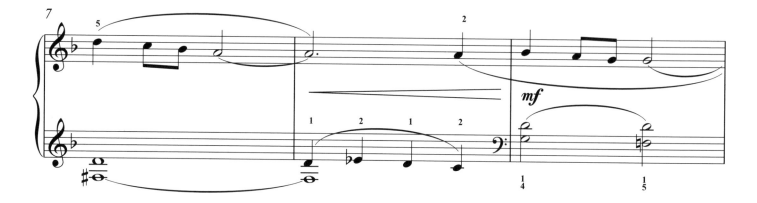

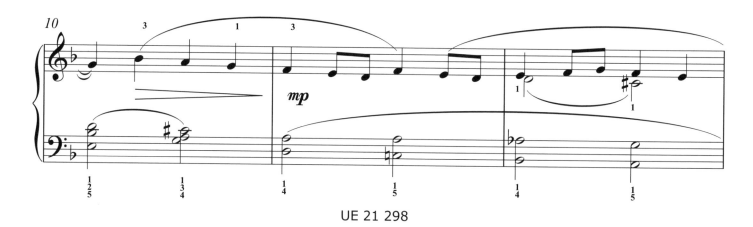

Kind of Calypso

Mike Cornick
(* 1947)

With a relaxed "8-beat" feel (♫ = ♩♪) ♩ = 126

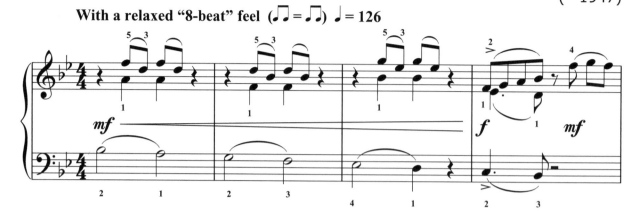

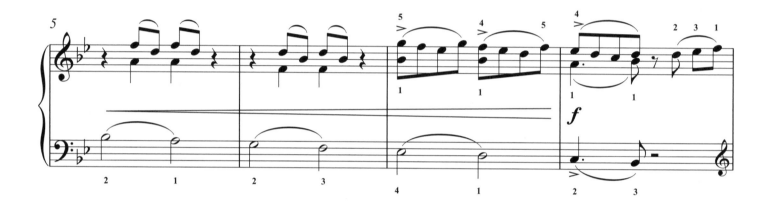

Sousse

Mike Cornick
(* 1947)

Distant Bells

Mike Cornick
(* 1947)

To Swing or Not to Swing...?

Mike Cornick
(* 1947)

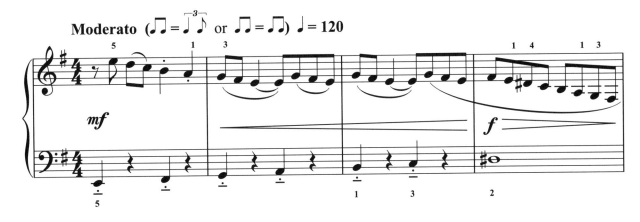

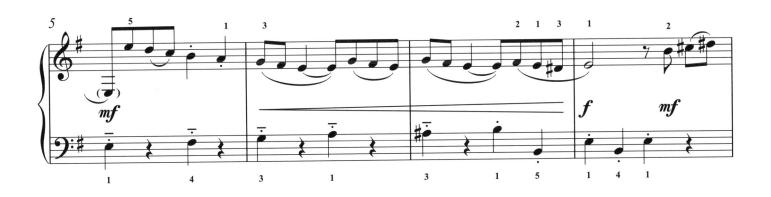

Scalic Blues

Mike Cornick
(* 1947)

Medium tempo swing (♫ = ♩♪) ♩ = 120

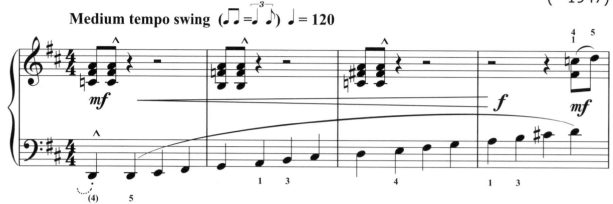

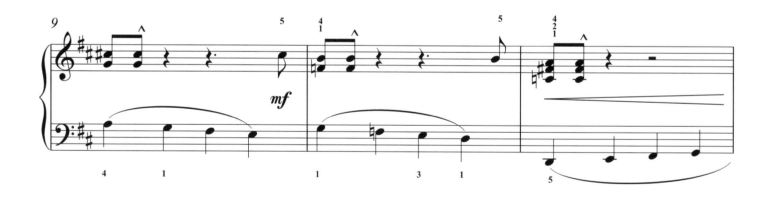

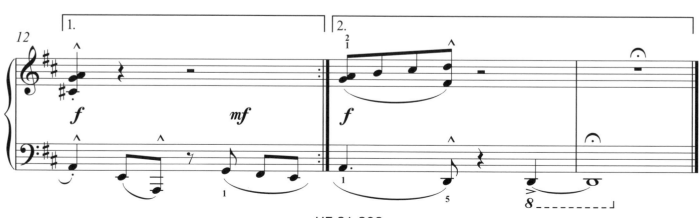

Pastorale

Mike Cornick
(* 1947)

With a gentle lilt ♩. = 44 (♪ = 132)

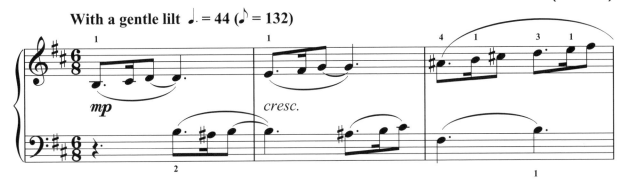

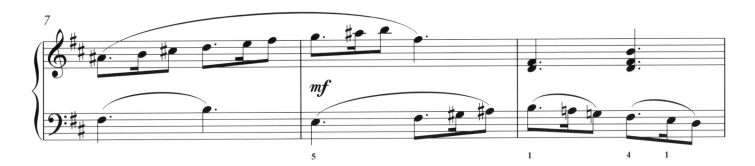

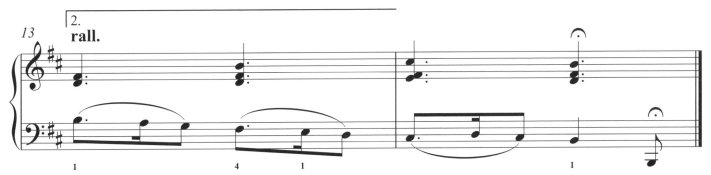

Chromatique Fantasia

Mike Cornick
(* 1947)

Lakeside

Mike Cornick
(* 1947)

Slowly and thoughtfully ♩ = 60
a tempo (on repeat)

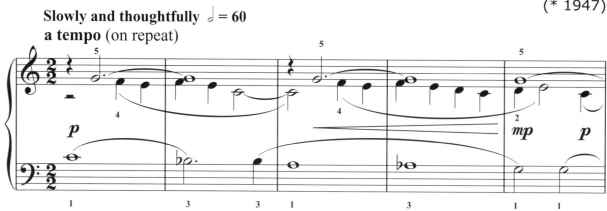

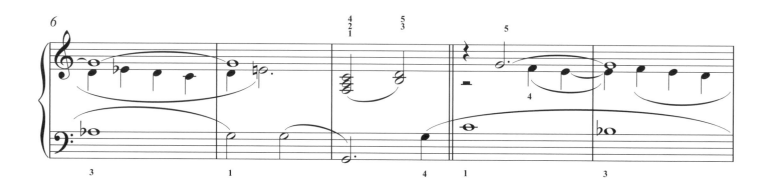

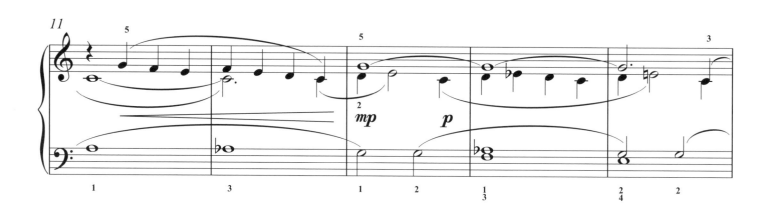

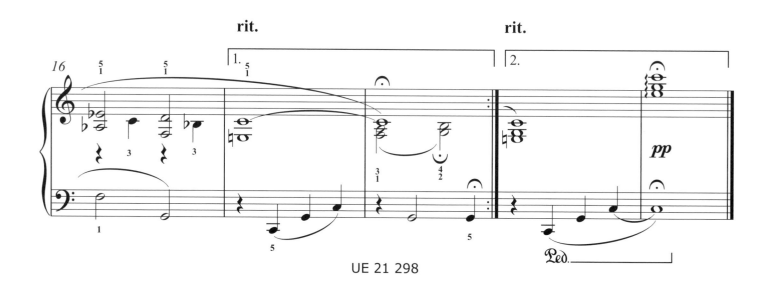

Aria for the Left Hand

Mike Cornick
(* 1947)

Staccato Pedal

Mike Cornick
(* 1947)

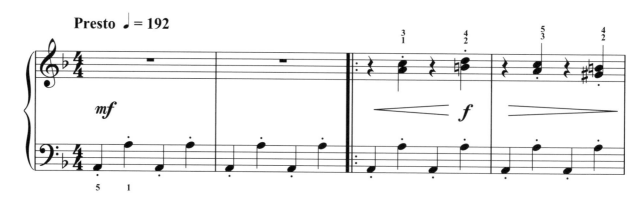

Serenata

Mike Cornick
(* 1947)

Andante cantabile (♫ = ♫) ♩ = 84

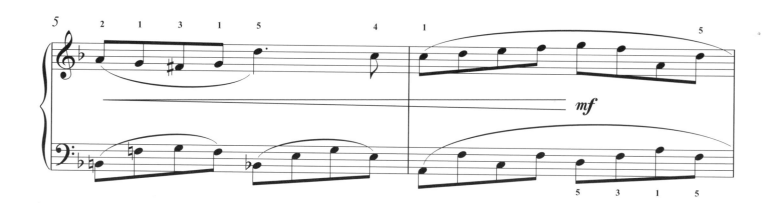

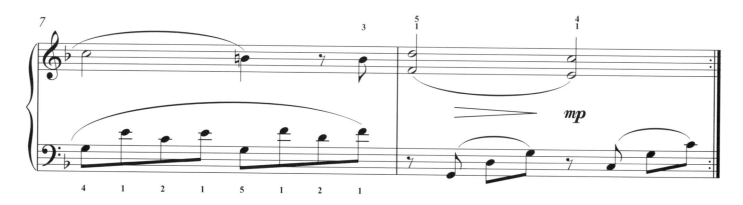

UE 21 298

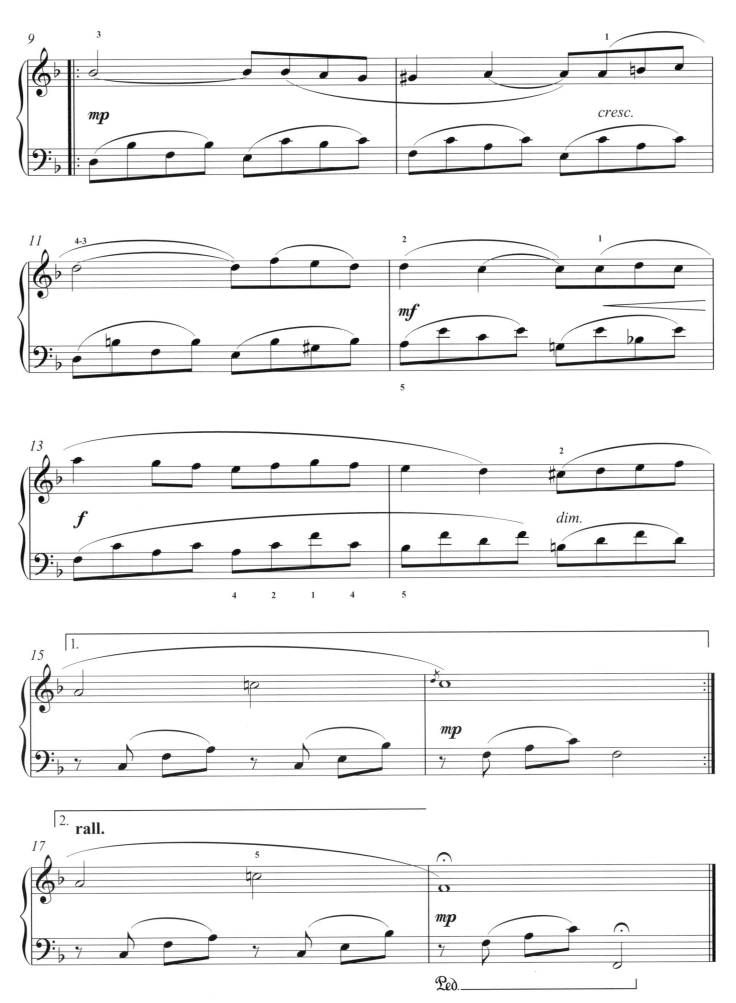

Bach to the Conga

Mike Cornick
(* 1947)

Chromatic Blues for the Left Hand

Mike Cornick
(* 1947)

Chromatic Blues for the Right Hand

Mike Cornick
(* 1947)

Left to Right!

Mike Cornick
(* 1947)

With an easy swing ♩ = 126

Right to Left!

Mike Cornick
(* 1947)

Incidental Blues

Mike Cornick
(* 1947)

Incidental Blues – 2

Mike Cornick
(* 1947)

With a "laid-back" swing feel (♫ = ♩ ♪) ♩ = 104

Incidental Blues – 3

Mike Cornick
(* 1947)

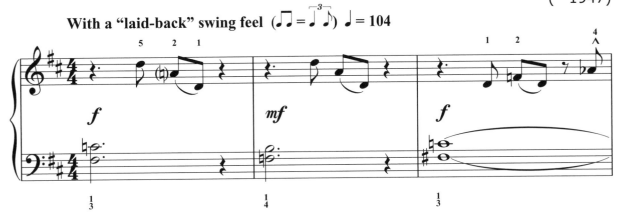

Three-Way Stretch

Mike Cornick
(* 1947)

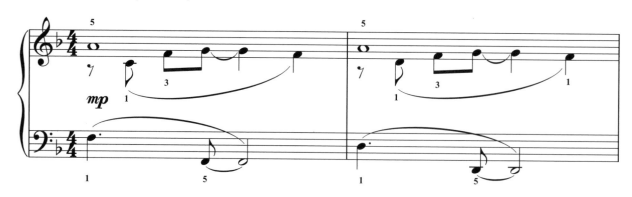

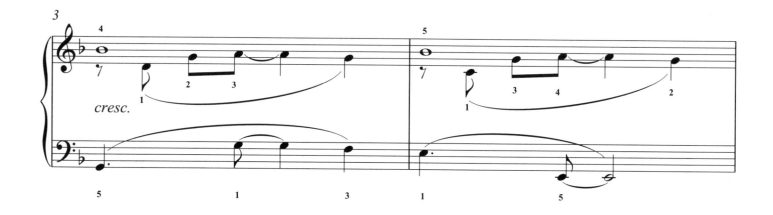

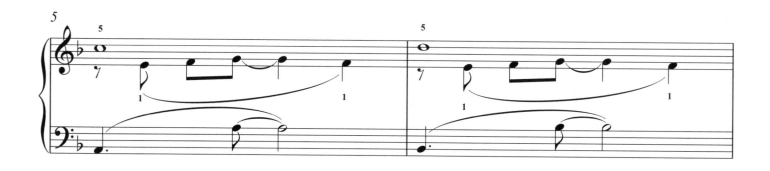

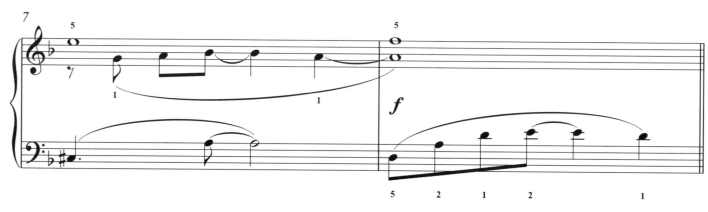

Starter's Samba

Mike Cornick
(* 1947)

With a steady latin feel ($\flat\flat = \flat\flat$) $\downarrow = 80$ ($\downarrow = 160$)

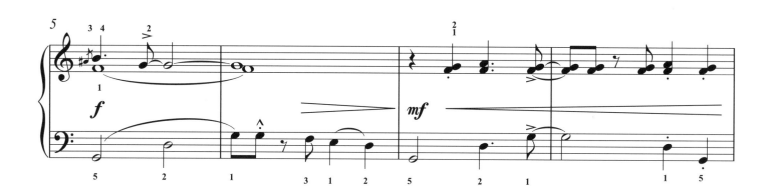

UE 21 298

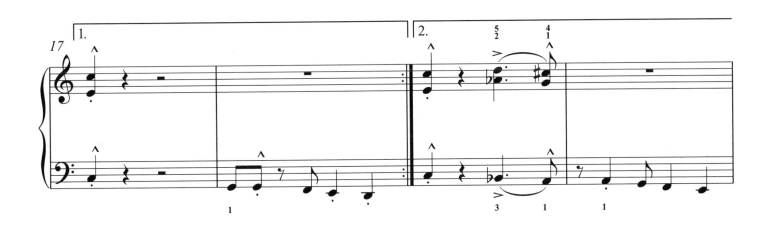

B Minor Waltz

Mike Cornick
(* 1947)

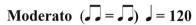

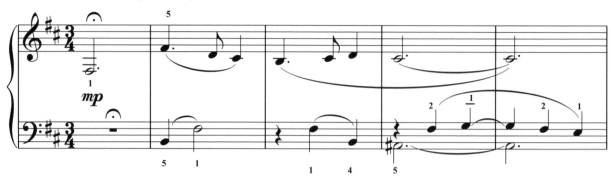

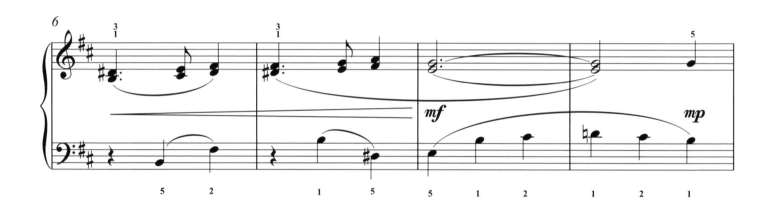

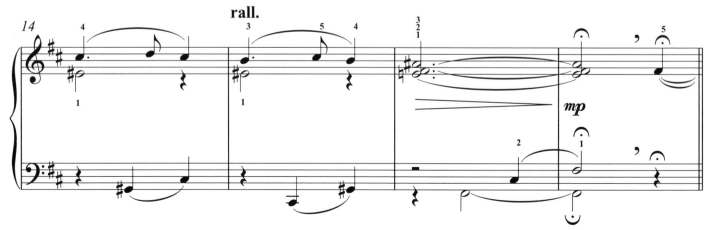

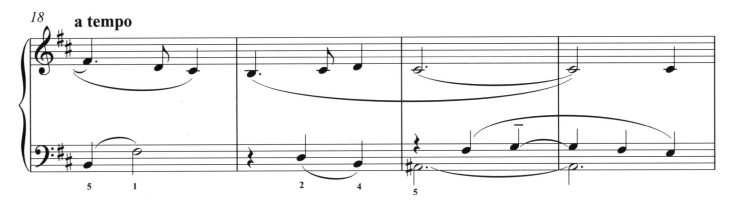

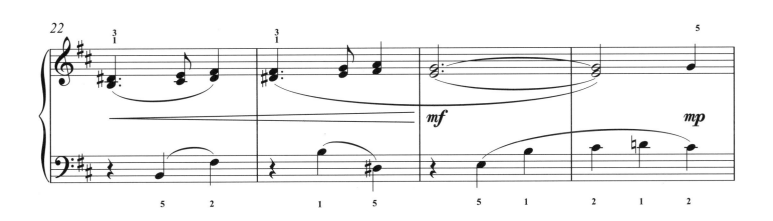

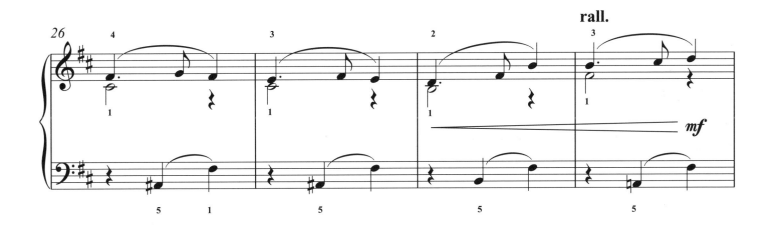

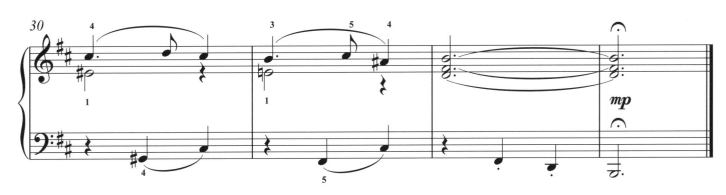

A Simple Song

Mike Cornick
(* 1947)

Ascension Rag

Mike Cornick
(* 1947)

At a steady ragtime tempo (♫ = ♫) ♩ = 126

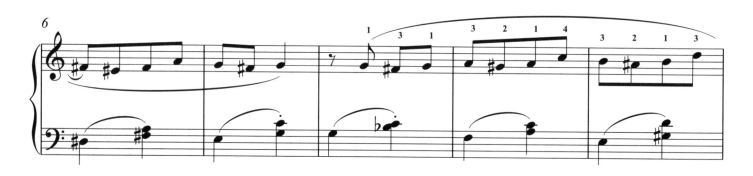

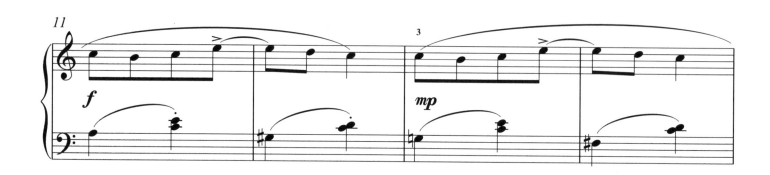

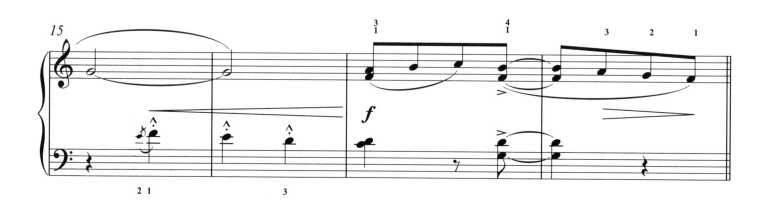

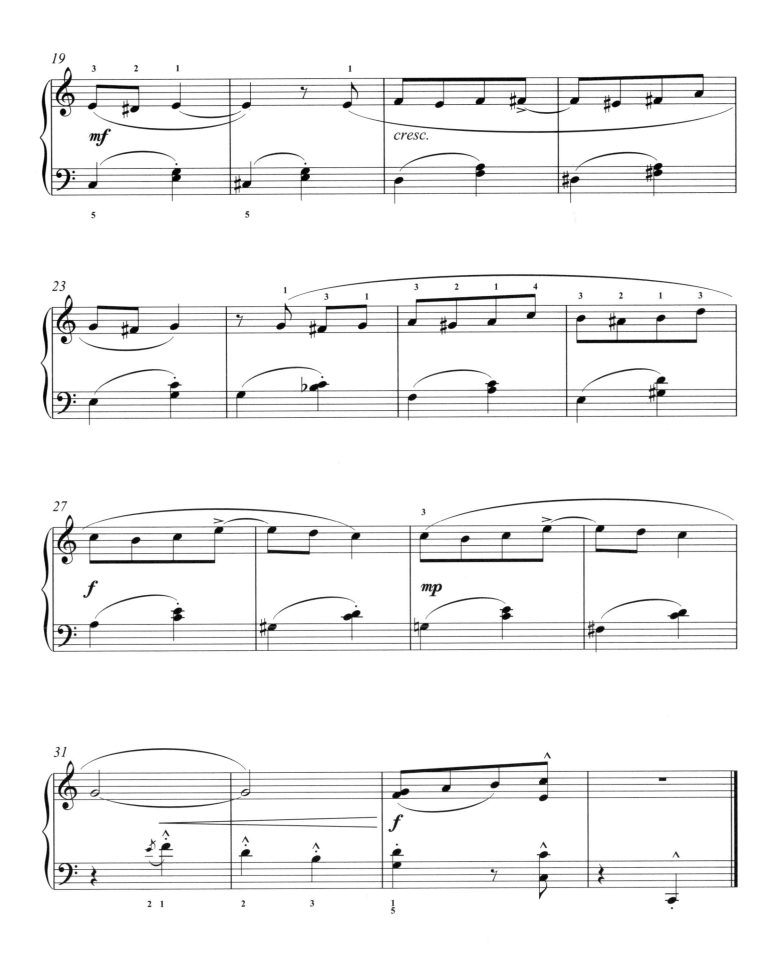

Little Siciliana

Mike Cornick
(* 1947)

With a gentle lilt ♩. = 40 (♪ = 120)

Dee for Dorian

Mike Cornick
(* 1947)

With a driving on-beat jazz-funk feel (♪♪ = ♪♪) ♩ = 130

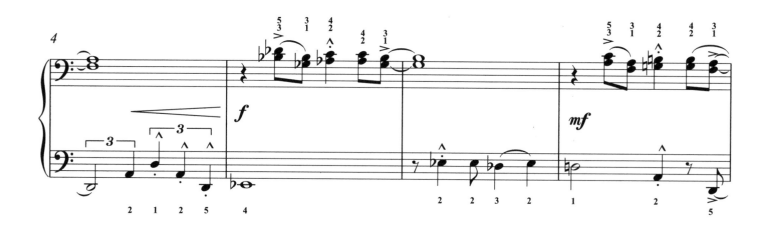

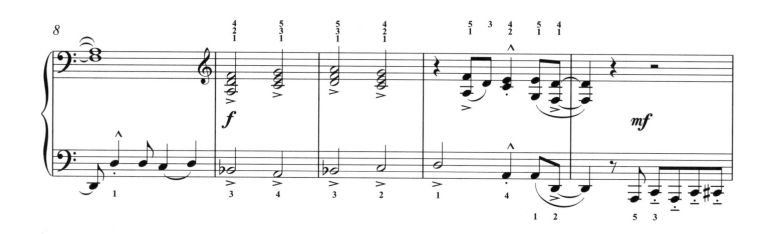

Mike Cornick
20 Piano Studies
in classical, jazz, rock
and latin style

Intermediate level
grade 4–5   UE 21 233